One to Grow On

Theodore Clymer

Olive Wong
Virginia Jones Benedict

Consultants
William E. Blanton EVALUATION
Milton D. Jacobson READABILITY
Ken Johnson LANGUAGE
Roger W. Shuy LINGUISTICS
E. Paul Torrance CREATIVITY

READING 720 READING 720
READING 720
READING 720
GINN
READING 720
READING 720
READING 720 READING 720

GINN AND COMPANY
A Xerox Education Company

Acknowledgments

Grateful acknowledgment is made to the following publishers, authors, and agents for permission to use and adapt copyrighted materials:

Rowena Bennett for the poem "The Steam Shovel" from her book *Story-Teller Poems.* Copyright by Rowena Bennett and used with her permission.

Carnegie Institution of Washington for "The Mud Horses," adapted from "The Poor Boy and the Mud Ponies" in Publication 59, *The Pawnee* by George A. Dorsey. Used by permission.

The Caxton Printers, Ltd., for "Yoko's Turn," adapted from "The Beautiful Mouse Girl" in *Japanese Folk Tales* by James E. O'Donnell. Used by permission.

Grossett & Dunlap, Inc., for the poem "The Clock," reprinted from *At the Top of My Voice and Other Poems* by Felice Holman. Text copyright © 1970 by Felice Holman. Published by Grosset & Dunlap, Inc.

Grove Press, Inc., for the poem "The Heel of My Thumb" by Mary Thomas, from *The Children: Poems and Prose from Bedford-Stuyvesant* edited by Irving Benig. Reprinted by permission of Grove Press, Inc. Copyright © 1971 by Irving Benig.

Harcourt Brace Jovanovich, Inc., for the poem "The Gnome" by Harry Behn from *Windy Morning,* copyright 1953, by Harry Behn. Reprinted by permission of Harcourt Brace Jovanovich, Inc. Also for the poem "Snow Toward Evening" from *So That It Flower* by Melville Cane. Copyright, 1926, by Harcourt Brace Jovanovich, Inc.; renewed, 1954, by Melville Cane. Reprinted by permission of the publishers.

Jack and Jill Magazine for the adaptation of "The Little Boy with the Big Name" by Dorothy Binder. Used with permission of *Jack and Jill* Magazine. Copyright 1966, by The Saturday Evening Post Co. Also for "Lucy's Smile," adapted from "Lucy Couldn't Smile" by Margaret Baur. Used with permission of *Jack and Jill* Magazine. Copyright 1965, by The Saturday Evening Post Co.

Friede Orleans Joffe for the poem "The Lost Balloon" by Ilo Orleans. From *Funday* by permission of Friede Orleans Joffe.

Lothrop, Lee & Shepard Co., Inc., for the text of *Grandfather and I* by Helen E. Buckley. Reprinted by permission of the publisher. Copyright © 1959 by Lothrop, Lee & Shepard Co., Inc.

Harold Ober Associates for the poem "City" by Langston Hughes from *The Langston Hughes Reader.* Reprinted by permission of Harold Ober Associates Incorporated. Copyright © 1958 by Langston Hughes.

Parents' Magazine Enterprises, Inc., for "The Boy and the Wolf" by Freya Littledale. Reprinted from *Humpty Dumpty's Magazine,* copyright © 1965 by The Better Reading Foundation. Permission granted by Parents' Magazine Enterprises, Inc.

Kris Ramseyer for her poem "Chocolate."

Random House, Inc., for the poem "David Likes to Fly His Kite" from *Poems Make Pictures,* by Giose Rimanelli and Paul Pimsleur. Copyright © 1972 by Giose Rimanelli and Paul Pimsleur. Reprinted by permission of Pantheon Books, a Division of Random House, Inc.

Mabel Watts for her story "Three in a Tree." Published originally in *Humpty Dumpty's Magazine,* February 1962. Adapted by permission of Mabel Watts.

World's Work Ltd of England for the text of *Grandfather and I* by Helen E. Buckley. Used by permission.

Contents

6

Like You or Me

Freckles

" Freckles ! Freckles ! " said Carlo.

" You stop it, Carlo, " said Mike.
" My name is not Freckles.
My name is Mike, Mike Parks. "

" You can't stop me ! " said Carlo.
" Freckles ! Freckles ! "

8

Mike looked at his face.
He didn't like what he saw.
His face did have freckles!
And Mike didn't like his freckles at all.

"Names! Names!" Mike said.
"Why do people have to make up names?
I can't help all the freckles!"

Mike made a face.

Mike saw Dad's shaving cream.
" Maybe this shaving cream
will help, " said Mike.
He put some on his face.
The freckles didn't go away.

Then Mike put something green
on his face.
   When he looked up, his freckles
looked back at him.

" Dad's shaving cream didn't help, "
said Mike.
   " All of this will not help.
Freckles ! I do NOT like freckles ! "

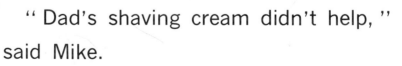

Dad came in.

" What are you doing ? " he asked.

" I don't like my freckles, Dad, "
said Mike.

" The boys call me names.

I put shaving cream and some of this
on my face.

But the freckles did not go away.

I don't want the boys to call me
Freckles. "

" I know, Mike, " said Dad.

" When I was a little boy,
I was a shorty.

The other boys liked to call me
Shorty—Shorty Parks. "

" Shorty Parks ? " asked Mike.

" But Dad, you aren't a shorty now !
You aren't a shorty at all. "

" I know, " said Dad.

" But sometimes boys like
to make fun of other boys.

Sometimes people say things we don't like. "

Mike had to smile.

He didn't like to be called Freckles.

But his dad had put up with Shorty—
Shorty Parks !

" Thanks, Dad, " said Mike
with a smile.

He whistled
and walked away.

The Heel of My Thumb

I love my thumb prints,
Nobody has my thumb prints,
Nobody, not nobody,
But myself, myself.
My brother has his own prints,
My mother's are almost like mine,
But I am glad they're not.
Mine will always be the same,
So will I be the same, forever
                    ever
                    ever
                    ever
                    ever
                    and
                    ever.

Mary Thomas

PAT'S SCHOOL PICTURE

"Where did you get all the pictures?"
called Pat.
"I see pictures here of all of you,
but I don't see mine!
Who took the pictures?"

"Miss White took the pictures
when you were out of school," said Mike.

It was time to read,
but Pat didn't look at his book.
He thought about the time
he was out of school.
He thought about the school pictures.
Pat wanted his picture up too!

The following day Pat ran
all the way to school.
He had thought of a way
to get his picture up.

When Pat got to school, he said,
" Here, Miss White.

This is a picture my dad took.

He took it the day I was out of school.

I'm going to put it up
with the other pictures. "

The children looked at Pat's picture.

" That's some picture, Pat, " said Mike.

" What can we name it ? " asked Miss White.

" We can call it PAT'S SCHOOL PICTURE, "
said Mike.

The children smiled.

They all liked that name.

The picture looked like this:

LUCY'S SMILE

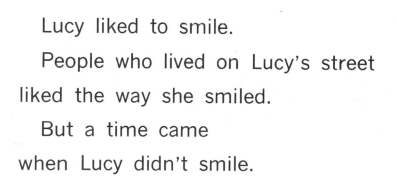

Lucy liked to smile.

People who lived on Lucy's street liked the way she smiled.

But a time came when Lucy didn't smile.

Lucy came down the street
on her way to school.

" Hello, Lucy, "
called Mr. Cunningham.

Lucy waved, but she did not smile.
Mr. Cunningham thought, " Lucy waved,
but I did not see her smile.
Where is Lucy's smile ? "

Mrs. Dandy saw Lucy.

"Hello, Lucy," Mrs. Dandy called.

Lucy waved to Mrs. Dandy.
She did not smile.

"Well," thought Mrs. Dandy.
"Where is Lucy's smile?"

Lucy came to school.
Some children called,
and Lucy waved back.
She did not smile at all.
The children looked at her
in surprise.
"Where is Lucy's smile?"
the children thought.

It was time to work.

Mr. Lee asked Lucy to read.

Lucy walked up to Mr. Lee
and said something to him.

"Lucy has a surprise for you,"
said Mr. Lee.

Lucy smiled at all the children.

"Why, Lucy!" Mr. Lee said.

"What a big smile!"

When the children looked at Lucy,
they smiled too.

Can you guess why Lucy
had not smiled?

What was her surprise?

THE MAGIC IN SEVEN

Lucy looked at her book,
but she wasn't reading it.

"Lucy," asked Mr. Lee.
"Are you reading?"

Lucy wanted to hide her face.
"It's my birthday, Mr. Lee,"
said Lucy. "I'm seven today!"

"A birthday today! Now I know why you are not reading," said Mr. Lee.
"So you are seven today!
Seven is magic, Lucy."

"Seven is magic?" asked Lucy.
"What's so magic about seven?"

"You will see," said Mr. Lee.

At last it was time to go home.
All the way Lucy thought about her birthday.
"Why is seven magic?" she thought.

Lucy looked up.

" That's funny, " she said.

" Here's my house . . .
77 Hill Street. "

Lucy walked
up to her apartment.
" Seven here too, "
thought Lucy.
" I live in Apartment Seven.
But that can't
be magic. "

Lucy went
into the apartment.
She had work to do.
" That's funny, " she thought.
" Seven people will eat here.
But that can't be magic. "

Mother and Dad and Lucy's
four brothers came home.

The four boys had a surprise
for Lucy.

It was for her birthday.

"A hamster!" said Lucy.
"Thank you! Thank you!
I like my hamster.
She will make a good pet."

That night Lucy didn't want
to go to sleep.

"This is a birthday
to remember," she thought.

"But what can be the magic
in this birthday?"

Lucy thought about her four brothers
and her pet hamster.

She thought about Apartment Seven
at 77 Hill Street.

She thought about the seven people
who lived in this apartment.

"I remember what
Mr. Lee said," thought Lucy.

"But what can be so magic
about all the sevens?"

At last Lucy went to sleep.

When it was time to get up,
Lucy went to look at the hamster.
" Mother ! Dad ! Come and see !
We have seven little hamsters ! "

Mother and Dad came.
Lucy's four brothers came too.
" Look ! " said Lucy.
" Look at all the little hamsters.
Seven IS magic ! "

May Ling's Pictures

May Ling lives in a building, on a
street, on a hill, in the city.
Down the street is a park.
Up the street is a school.

In the morning, May Ling and her two
brothers and sister go up the hill to school.

31

After school, May Ling's brothers and sister run down the hill to play in the park.

But not May Ling.

She has something to do.

May Ling runs up the steps of her building and into the house.

She picks up her things.

Then she starts to work.

May Ling makes pictures.

Sometimes she sits on the steps and
makes pictures of people going by, or of
the stores on the other side of the street.

And sometimes she makes pictures of cars.

Sometimes she sits in her father's
bookstore and makes pictures of the places,
animals, and people in the books.

Sometimes she makes pictures at
the playground where her mother works.

Pictures, pictures, pictures are
May Ling's work and play.

Her brothers and sister make fun of her.

They say things like—

" Why are you making pictures ? "

" Don't you get sick of pictures ? "

" What good are they ? "

But May Ling doesn't care.

She just works on her pictures.

One day, May Ling runs down the hill
to the park with her brothers and sister.

They are surprised.

" What ? No pictures today ? " they say.

" Come on. You will see, " says May Ling.

There are people and pictures all
over the park.

People are looking at pictures.

People are making pictures too.

And there on a big wall are
all of May Ling's pictures.

"See," she says.

"Now what do you think of my pictures?"

"Look at that!" they say.
That was all they could say.
But now they say things like—
"May Ling, will you make a picture
of my kitten?"

"May Ling, help me make a picture
of a truck."

"You make good pictures, May Ling."

Dr. Penny

It was Saturday and there was no school.
Rose was playing under the trees
near her house.

" Beep, beep. " Rose looked up.
It was a red car.
In the car was Dr. Penny.

Rose ran to the car.

" Hi, Rose, " said Dr. Penny.

" How is your leg ? "

" Fine, " said Rose.

She put out her leg.

The big cut that Dr. Penny had fixed was well.

All you could see was a little line.

" It's good to see you walking again, " said Dr. Penny.

" You were in bed a long time. "

Dr. Penny was a good doctor.

All of Rose's friends went to her
when they were sick.

Dr. Penny worked in the city.

Rose's mother came outside.

" It's good to see you, Dr. Penny, " she said.

" What are you doing out here ? " asked Rose.

" I came out to make a house call, but
I'm lost, " said Dr. Penny.

" Lost ? " said Rose.

" Yes, " said Dr. Penny.

" I've been looking for Dan Fox's house for
a long, long time.

Do you know where he lives ? "

" Oh, you're not lost, Dr. Penny, "
said Rose.

" I do know where he lives.
Do you want me to take you to his house ? "

" Could you, Rose ? " said Dr. Penny.

" Yes, could we walk ? " Rose said.
" It's faster that way. "

" Fine, " said Dr. Penny.

Rose's mother said, "Come back when you finish.

We can have something to eat."

"I'll do that," said Dr. Penny.
Dr. Penny got her bag from the car.
Then she and Rose walked to the school.

"If we go through the playground and over the hill, we can see the house," said Rose.
And it was just as Rose said.

Billy Fox was playing with some children.

His father was waiting near the house.

" I'm glad to see you, Dr. Penny, "
said Mr. Fox.

" I thought maybe you got lost. "

" Oh, I did get lost, but then I saw Rose, "
said Dr. Penny.

" Rose knew the way. "

" Hi, Rose, " said Billy and his father.

Rose said, " Hi, Mr. Fox. Hi, Billy. "

Dr. Penny walked to the house with
Mr. Fox.

" I'll play out here, " said Rose.

" Then we can walk back to my house when
you finish. "

People You Know

Here are some of the people you met in your stories.

Read the following words.
Then look at the pictures.
Can you name the boy or girl
each word makes you think of?

smile	Dad	seven
bookstore	apartment	shaving cream
birthday	playground	Dr.
freckles	picture	school

In what ways are these people
like boys and girls you know?
Do you like Mike, Lucy, Pat, Rose
or May Ling the best? Why?

Using a Map

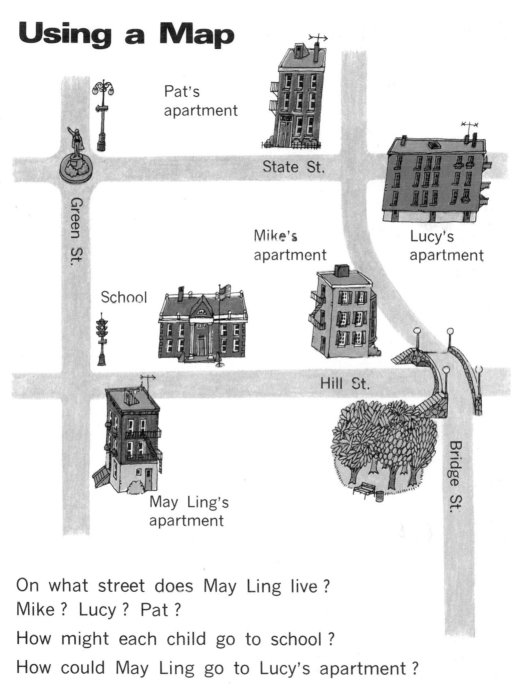

On what street does May Ling live?
Mike? Lucy? Pat?

How might each child go to school?

How could May Ling go to Lucy's apartment?
Mike to Pat's? Pat to May Ling's?

45

46

Balloons, Balloons, and More Balloons

The School Fair

Bill whistled and walked
down the steps of Anders School.
This was one day when the school
did not look like a school at all.
It was the day of the school fair.

Mr. Ball had come to do
some magic at the fair.

Bozo was there to make
the children smile.

There was something
for Bill to do at the fair too.

He would be helping
Mr. Mays with the balloons.

"Right this way!" Bill called.
"Balloons! Balloons!
Get your balloons here!"

There was a balloon for every boy
and every girl at Anders School.

Every balloon had a postcard with it.
The postcard said:

This balloon came to you from
the children at the Anders School.
Please mail the postcard back
to the school. We want to know
who you are and where you live.
Thank you

Mr. Mays let one balloon go.

Then he called to the children,

" Let the balloons go ! "

The children thought about the people
who would get the balloons.

Who could they be ?

What fun it would be when the postcards
came back in the mail !

The children could not wait !

Kay

A postcard came in the mail.
It was from a little girl named Kay.
It said:

I live in the woods.
My Dad is a lumberman.
I am mailing a surprise
for all the children at
the Anders School. Kay

Late that day
the surprise came.
It was a small yellow book.
Kay had made it
with her dad's help.
It was about the woods
and about lumbering.

Kay's Book

My dad works here in the woods.
Every day he goes into the woods.
He tags the tall trees that are
to come down.

Men come along
with saws.
They cut down
the tall trees.
Other men come along
to cut the tall trees
into logs.

Big trucks go
into the woods.
The logs are put
onto the trucks.
Then the trucks take the logs
to the sawmill.
At the sawmill, the logs are put
into a log pond.

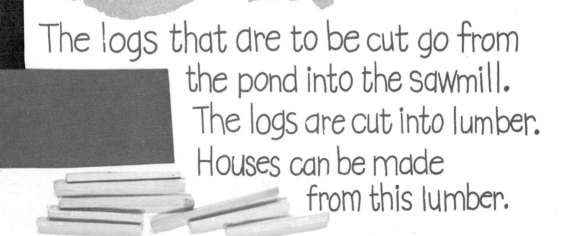

57

The logs that are to be cut go from the pond into the sawmill. The logs are cut into lumber. Houses can be made from this lumber.

boys and girls: please read
this reply

Kay's
Book

My dad works here in the woods.
Every day he goes into the woods.
He tags the tall trees that are
to come down.

Men come along
with saws.
They cut down
the tall trees.
Other men come along
to cut the tall trees
into logs.

Mr. Mays put Kay's small yellow book
where all the children could see it.

" That was a good surprise, " said Bill.

" It would be fun to live
in the woods like that.

It would be fun to see a lumberman
cut the tall trees into logs. "

" Where do you think the other balloons
went ? " asked the children.

" I don't know, " said Mr. Mays.

" The other postcards will have
to answer that. "

58

A Balloon That Works

Far from Anders School, Mrs. Towns
was working with a balloon.

This balloon was not a toy.

This balloon was a weather balloon.

It would find out about the weather
far up in the sky.

Mrs. Towns let the big weather balloon go.

In no time at all it was far up
over the trees.

All at once Mrs. Towns saw something!

The big weather balloon was going up into the sky.

A little red balloon was on its way down from the sky.

The little red balloon had a postcard with it.

" Look at this ! " Mrs. Towns called
to the other workers.

" Here's a postcard from some children
in a city far away.

They want to know who we are,
and where we live. "

A worker smiled and said,
" Why not hand that postcard
over to me ?

My boy Sandy can answer this.

He can let the children know
about weather balloons. "

This balloon came to you from
the children at the Anders School.
Please mail the postcard back
to the school. We want to know
who you are and where you live.
Thank you.

Dear Boys and Girls,
   In a box under the balloon
are weather instruments.
   The instruments find out
about the weather on the
way into space.

← balloon

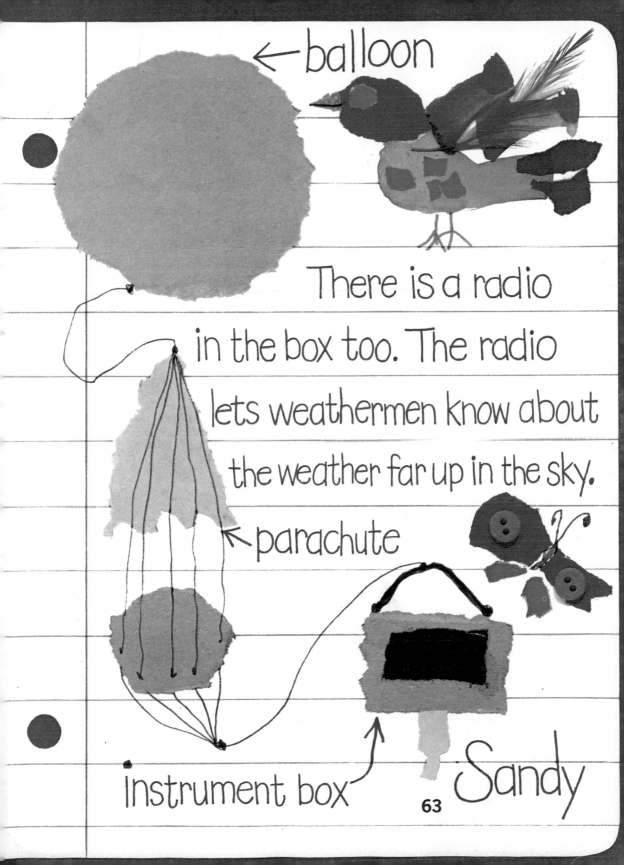

There is a radio in the box too. The radio lets weathermen know about the weather far up in the sky.

← parachute

Instrument box

Sandy

64

David likes to fly his kite on a windy day. He likes to watch it as it sails far up into the skyyyyyyyyyyyyy.

Giose Rimanelli and
Paul Pimsleur

Sky House

Donna liked to be up
on the roof of the apartment house.
When the weather was fair,
she and her brother Don could play there.
Donna called the roof
" Sky House. "

66

From the roof the children
could look far down on the city.
Big cars looked like little cars.
Little cars looked like ants.
Don said the trucks looked like toys.

Sometimes the children
came to Sky House at night.

Then they could see the lights of the city.

Donna liked to see the lights on helicopters.

On and off, on and off, went the lights
in the night sky.

Don liked to look off into space.

He thought the lights
in the night sky made magic pictures.

One day Donna thought she saw a ship
far away from Sky House.

Don was about to look too,
when he saw something.

"Donna! Donna!" he called.

"Come here right away.

I think I see a balloon!"

"It **is** a balloon!"
said Donna in surprise.

"And there's a postcard with it!"

Don and Donna read the postcard
from the children at the Anders School.

"I know what we can say on the postcard,"
said Donna.

"I know too," said Don.

"The children at this school would like
to know about Sky House."

AIR MAIL

Nan was a little girl
who could not go to school.
She couldn't run and hop
and jump with the other children.
But every day school came to Nan!
Every day Miss Green came
to help Nan with her schoolwork.

And every day Mr. Migs
came with the mail.

Long before he came,
Nan was waiting for him.

At the other houses Mr. Migs
would put the mail in the boxes.

But not at Nan's house!

When mail came for Nan, Mr. Migs
took it right to her.

Once a letter came from Nan's grandmother,
who lived a long way off.

Other letters came from children
who could go to school.

Before Mr. Migs went on, he would ask Nan
about her schoolwork.

Nan would ask Mr. Migs
about the weather.

One day Nan was doing her schoolwork
for Miss Green.

As she was working, she saw Mr. Migs
stop at the mailboxes on her street.

Nan waved, and Mr. Migs waved too.

Before long Nan finished her schoolwork.

" Maybe Mr. Migs has some mail
for me today, " thought Nan.

She looked up. There in the sky
was a little red balloon.

Down, down it came.

"Mr. Migs!
Mr. Migs!"
Nan called.
"Please get that balloon for me."

Mr. Migs took the red balloon to her.

He and Nan read the postcard
from Anders School.

"What a surprise!" said Nan.

"It's a surprise all right,"
said Mr. Migs.

"It's a funny way to get mail too.

Guess you could say this postcard
came by **air mail!**"

Mr. Migs smiled and went on
with his work.

Nan went to work too.

She had some air mail
to answer.

THE LOST BALLOON

A little boy
Was careless once,
   And lost his yellow
   Toy balloon.
It flew up high
And reached the sky
   And ever since
   It's called the moon.

Ilo Orleans

76

More about Balloons

A long, long time ago, some men were sitting around a fire.

They were looking at smoke going up into the air.

This made them think.

Could smoke make a bag go up too?

The men wanted to see.

They took a bag and held it over the smoke.

The warm air made the bag go up into the sky.

77

Then the men made a **big** bag.

Under this first balloon

they put a basket.

In the basket they put a pan.

In the pan was a fire.

The fire made the air warm.

The warm air

made the big balloon go up too!

The men made one more balloon.

It, too, had a basket and a pan.

There was a fire in the pan.

But this time there was something new.

In the basket were a duck, a rooster,
and a sheep.

When the balloon went up into the sky,
the animals went too.

When the balloon came down,
the animals were safe.

That same year, people, too, went up
into the sky in a balloon.

Then more men and women went up
in balloons.

They began to learn many things.

People learned about weather.

They began to take pictures from balloons.

People made maps by looking down
from balloons.

And people in balloons learned about space.
They went higher and higher in balloons.
Balloons helped people get ready
for the space age.

Sending Messages

1. How could you send a message to a friend?
   What kind of message could you send
   each of these ways?

2. How might you send a message if you
   wanted a stranger to find it?
   What information would you send and what
   would you want the person to send back?

3. What other ways can you think of
   to send a message?

Can You Get to the Top?

Can you reach the balloon
without missing a rung?
First try one ladder.
Then try another.

law	hot	loon
thaw	got	noon
saw	dot	soon
jaw	lot	moon
paw	stop	cool
stall	chop	pool
fall	shop	tool
hall	mop	boot
wall	pop	hoot
ball	top	toot

E. WEST ST.

86

World of the City

87

In the morning the city
Spreads its wings
Making a song
Of stone that sings.

In the evening the city
Goes to bed
Hanging lights
About its head.

Langston Hughes

SIGHTS OF THE CITY

See the Sights!

See the Sights!

"See the sights!" called the tall man.
Every day the tall man came
to 5th Street.
Every day he called, "See the sights!
See the sights!"

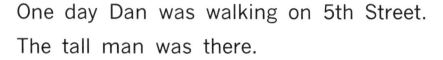

One day Dan was walking on 5th Street.

The tall man was there.

He was calling, " See the sights !
See the sights ! "

Dan saw a big sight-seeing bus stop
on 5th Street.

There was a sign on the back
of the bus.

The sign said, " See the Sights !
See the Sights ! "

" What sights ?
Where does that bus go ? " Dan thought.

The next day Dan walked
up to the tall man.

"I want to see the sights," he said.

"When can I take the bus?"

"You're too late today," said the man.

"Come back next Saturday.

Saturday you can see the sights!"

The next Saturday Dan got
on the big sight-seeing bus.

He was happy, for at last
he was going to see the sights.

As the bus made its way
down the street, a man talked
to the people.

Dan did not know streets
could go so many ways!

Some went up, and some went down.

Some went under other streets.

What fun it was seeing
the many sights of the city!

Dan Sees the City

The bus made its first stop
at a big red building.

Dan and the other people
got off the bus.

They went up
into the big red building.

What a sight this was!
Dan saw many, many animals
in this building.

Where did animals like this come from ?

When did they live ?

Dan couldn't remember seeing animals so big before.

95

Next the bus came to the harbor.

Dan could see
big, **big** ships
and little, little boats.

Ships and boats,
big and little—
everywhere in the harbor.

He could see
  people working
  and people building.
He could see
  people coming and going,
  coming and going
  everywhere.

The next stop was the city airport.

Dan saw a big jet take off.

What a noise it made!

Far up into

the sky went the jet.

Other jets took off

into the blue sky.

What a noise!

A man from the airport building talked to Dan and the others.

Dan asked about the big jet.

The man said it took people to a country far away.

"I want to go on a jet," said Dan.

"Maybe you will someday," the man said with a smile.

At last it was time to go home.

The bus took Dan and the others past apartments and stores.

It took them past cars and people.

When the bus came to 5th Street, Dan got off.

The other people on the bus could see a happy smile on his face.

They didn't know his name.

But they did know he was happy.

He had seen the sights of the city!

5TH STREET

100

SNOW TOWARD EVENING

Suddenly the sky turned gray,
The day,
Which had been bitter and chill,
Grew soft and still.
Quietly
From some invisible blossoming tree
Millions of petals cool and white
Drifted and blew,
Lifted and flew,
Fell with the falling night.

Melville Cane

snow

Snow came to the city.

It came when the city was sleeping.

Softly, softly it came in the night.

White flakes fell on buildings
and streets.

White, white flakes of snow
on all the city.

All the city—soft and white
in the night.

When daylight came, the snow
was pretty and white.

But it did not stay pretty
on the streets.

Before long workers came.

They took the snow away
in trucks.

The policeman did not like
working in the snow.

He could not keep all the cars
going.

The people in the cars
did not like the snow.

They didn't want to stay
on the street all morning.

They wanted to keep going.

They wanted to get to work
on time.

But the children liked the snow.

They liked to put on red boots.

They liked to walk in the snow.

They liked to make snowballs.

Red boots ! White snowballs !

Red boots in the white snow !

White flakes on green trees !

What a pretty sight !

The children walked
in the park.

The snow was soft and white
on the trees.

" It looks pretty here in the park, "
a girl said softly.

The other children didn't answer.

They walked on to school
in the soft white snow.

A Real Movie

"Juan! Juan!"
Juan looked out.
It was Lola calling.
"Do you want to be in a movie?" asked Lola.

"A movie?" said Juan. "What movie?"

"Come see," said Lola.

Juan came out of the building.

"They're making a movie on Pine Street,"
said Lola.

"See that big thing over there."
Juan looked.

"That's one of the lights," said Lola.

"Come on."

Lola and Juan ran over to Pine Street.

Pine Street didn't look the same.

There were people running around.

There were two big vans.

The street had many lines
of black cable.

There were poles with big lights.

And there was a new red car.

" There they are, " said Lola.

Juan saw all his friends talking

to a woman.

" This is Juan, " Lola said to the woman.

" Hello, Juan, " said the woman.

" We're about to begin.

Please sit down. "

Juan sat down with the others.

" My name is Ana.

This is what I want you to do. "

Ana held a black slate in her hand.
" In the movie, you are sitting here.
Maybe you're just home from school.
You're talking and playing, " she said.

" Now do you see the red car ?
When I wave, it's going to come here.
You don't see it at first, " said Ana.

" Then, Lola, you see it and say,
' He's coming. He's coming. '

" Then all of you stop what you're doing.
The car will stop and you look inside
and say, ' Pepe ! Pepe ! ' "

"Can you remember that?" asked Ana.

"Yes!" they said.

"Let's do it then," said Ana.

They began to talk.
Ana waved.
The car came up the street.
Lola said her lines, and they ran up
to the car.
"Pepe! Pepe!" they said.

Inside the car was a man.
"Are you Pepe?" asked Juan.

The man smiled.
"I'm Pepe," he said.

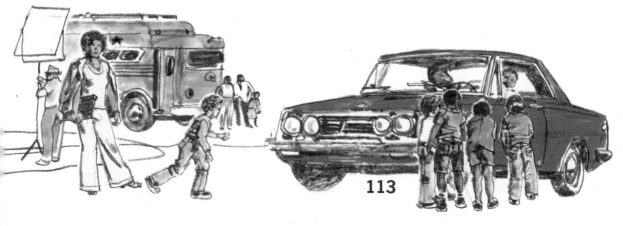

Ana came over.

" That was very, very good, " she said.

" Now can we do it with lights ? " asked Lola.

" Yes, " said Ana. " With the lights. "

The red car went back down the street
with Pepe.

The big lights were put in place.

The big vans came up to take the pictures.

The lines of black cable went up
on the poles.

" Ready ? " said Ana.

" Ready, " they said.

" Lights ! Camera ! Action ! " said Ana
as she closed the slate.

They were making a movie.
A real movie.

FUN IN THE SUN

Sandy and her brother Sam
walked down the street.

The sun made the city hot, too hot
to run and play.

" Am I hot ! " said Sam.

" Can we go to the park ? "

" Yes, " Sandy answered.

" It's too hot to stay here. "

117

"Sam! Look, Sam!" Sandy called
to her brother.

"It's Mr. Snow!"

The children ran to a little
green car that had just come
down the street.

"Hello, Sam. Hello, Sandy,"
said Mr. Snow.

"Thought you would like me
to come and help you cool off
on this hot day."

118

"Cool off! Who can cool off
when the sun is this hot?" Sam asked.
"Your name is cool,
but that's about all that is cool
in the city today."

Mr. Snow smiled at Sam.
"Look down the street," he said.

Sam and Sandy saw
a long red truck stop in the street.
    A man in the truck waved
to the children.

    " That man is going to make
you cool, " said Mr. Snow.
    " He will let the water run
in the street.
    It will cool you off,
and wash the street too ! "

Other children came out
to play in the wet street.
They splashed and splashed
in the cool water.

" Come down here, Sandy, "
called Sam.
" Come down and get splashed ! "

But Sandy was not looking
at Sam or Mr. Snow or the other children.
She was looking up over the roof
of the apartment house.

"What a pretty sight!" she said.

Mr. Snow came over to look.

Some of the other children

came over too.

But not Sam.

He didn't want to look.

He liked being where he was
with the cool water splashing
over him.

It was good to be wet and cool
on this hot day.

For Fun

Have you ever seen – – –

1. a bug on a rug with a mug ?

2. chalk on the walk that could talk ?

3. ten men in a pen with a hen ?

4. a bun having fun in the sun ?

5. a dog with a hog and a frog ?

6. the top of a mop try to hop ?

Read these sentences.
The missing word will end with the same
sounds as the name of the picture.

1. We will put a small

    in this little white _____ .

2. You may find a

    in the light of the _____ .

3. When you ride in a

    you may put on a _____ .

124

What Is a City?

There are many cars and buses in a city.
You can look down on a city and see many
tall buildings and the streets around them.
And you can see many things being made
by many workers.

1. Do tall buildings make a city?

2. Do workers make a city?

3. Do cars and buses make a city?

   What is a city, then?

126

Could It Be?

Mother Time

Mother Time fixed clocks.

She had a small shop with clocks from wall to wall.

She had clocks up to the roof.

Mother Time was busy fixing clocks.

She had something to fix all the time.

She was so busy that she had not learned to tell time.

That's right.

Mother Time couldn't tell time.

She could fix the insides of clocks.

But she didn't know how to tell time.

No one knew that Mother Time couldn't tell time.

She didn't want anyone to know, so she didn't even tell Linda.

Linda helped Mother Time.
She could fix clocks too.
Mother Time had helped her learn.

One day Mother Time thought that she
would trick Linda.
She thought that she could play a
game that would make Linda teach her
to tell time.

That day when Linda came in from school,
Mother Time said, " Why don't we play
a game today?

Then you can practice telling time, and
I'll get my shop cleaned. "

They lined up the clocks.

As they put a clock in place, Linda would
read the time.

Mother Time watched.

Just as they were going to put the last
of the clocks away, Mother Time said,
" I'll read the time on these clocks. "
And she did.
Mother Time said the right time
for each clock.
She was so happy.

When Linda went home to eat,
Mother Time said, "Thank you for helping
me clean the shop."

And Linda said, "I had a good time.
It was fun to teach you to tell time."

133

Mr. Harvey's Hat

Mr. Harvey was so pleased with his new hat!
He walked out of his apartment house
and on down the street.
" My, my !
What a wind !
In this wind my new hat may not— "

With that off went Mr. Harvey's hat.

The wind had made the hat
fly down the street.

"Stop! Stop!" Mr. Harvey called.

But the wind blew and blew.

It made the new hat fly on and on
down the street.

Mr. Harvey's hat blew far, far away.

That day a farmer had come
into the city in his truck.

Now he was going home.

As the truck came to a stoplight,
Mr. Harvey's hat came flying down.

The new hat blew
right into the farmer's truck.

Before long the truck was
on its way once more.

And so was Mr. Harvey's hat!

The truck went away
from the buildings of the city.

It went far out
into the country.

At last the truck came to a stop
in a cool barn.

A big blackbird looked down
from the top of the barn.

He could see the top of Mr. Harvey's hat
in the back of the truck.

"A hat!" thought the blackbird.

"I know something I can do with that!"

The blackbird took the hat
from the truck.

In no time at all
he was flying out of the barn
and over to the farmer's scarecrow.

He put the hat on top
of the scarecrow.

" Now I will know the farmer
from the scarecrow, " said the blackbird.

He smiled as he thought of the trick
he had played on the farmer.

The next Saturday Mr. and Mrs. Harvey
went for a ride.

Mr. Harvey's green car
left the tall buildings
and apartment houses of the city.

Soon Mr. and Mrs. Harvey
were far out in the country.

" Look over there, " said Mrs. Harvey.
" Look at that funny scarecrow
in the farmer's garden.

He has on a hat like yours ! "

Mr. Harvey stopped the car.

He looked at the hat

on top of the scarecrow.

"That looks just like—

but it couldn't be!

How could my new hat get out here?"

Then, without waiting for an answer,
Mr. Harvey smiled.

"That is not my hat—
not my hat at all," he said.

"Let's keep going.

It's a good day for a ride
in the country!"

The Little Boy with the Big Name

The little boy
on the white fence was unhappy.

It was his name that made him unhappy.

Bradford Underwood Timothy Charles
Hoppenpopper.

How would you like to have a long name
like his ?

" Why can't I have a name like other boys ? "
he thought.

He wanted to leave out some of his names.

But he couldn't leave out Hoppenpopper,
for this was his last name.

Great-grandfather's name was Charles.

He couldn't leave out that name.

Grandfather's name was Timothy,
so he couldn't leave out Grandfather's name.

Underwood had been Mother's name,
so he couldn't leave out Underwood.

And he couldn't leave out Bradford,
for that was his dad's name.

" What can I do ? " thought the boy.

A wise old owl was in the tree
over the white fence.

The owl was so wise, he could read
the thoughts of the unhappy boy.

"I can help you,"
said Wise Old Owl.

"How can you help me?" asked the boy.

"I know you are wise,
but what can you do about my name?"

"Do as I say," said Wise Old Owl.

"Go home and get some paper.

Put down on the paper the first letters
of all your names.

Then you will have a new name."

Bradford Underwood Timothy Charles
Hoppenpopper couldn't wait to see
his new name.

He jumped down from the fence
and ran all the way home.

One at a time, he put down on paper
the first letters of all his names.

Then Bradford Underwood Timothy
Charles Hoppenpopper smiled a big smile.

Do you know what the letters
on the paper said ?

Now .... has a new name,
and he is not unhappy at all !

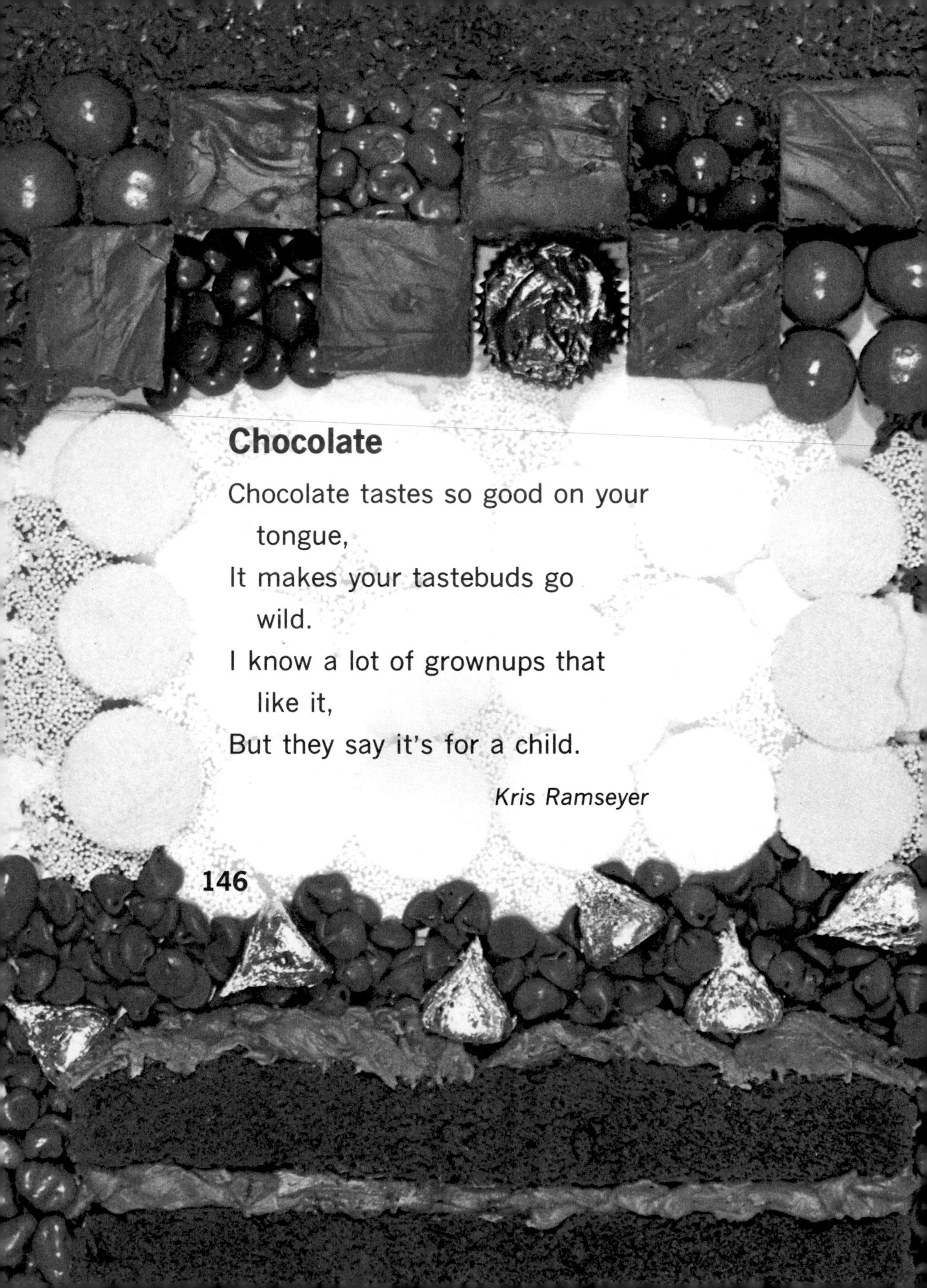

Chocolate

Chocolate tastes so good on your
   tongue,
It makes your tastebuds go
   wild.
I know a lot of grownups that
   like it,
But they say it's for a child.

Kris Ramseyer

146

Three in a Tree

An eagle, a cat, and a pig lived
in a tree in the woods.
Eagle lived at the top of the tree.
Cat lived under Eagle.
Pig lived under Cat.
They liked to live this way.
Three in a tree!

When Eagle wanted something,
he would call down to Cat.

When Cat wanted something,
he would call down to Pig.

When Pig wanted something,
he would call up to all the others.

Yes, it was good to live this way.
Three in a tree!

One morning Cat wanted to sleep,
but he couldn't.

Eagle was going in and out, in and out
of the tree top.

Pig made funny noises from his home
in the tree.

" How can I sleep here ? " said Cat.

Up, up the tree he went.

"See here, Eagle!" said Cat.

"I think Pig is unhappy
with all this going in and out, in and out."

"If Pig is unhappy, why can't he
call up here and say so?" asked Eagle.

But Cat didn't answer.
He was on his way down the tree
to see Pig.

"What is it?" asked the pig
when he saw Cat.

"Eagle does not like
the funny noises you make," said Cat.

"If Eagle is unhappy with me,
why can't he come down here and say so?"

But Cat did not answer.
He went on into the woods
to get something to eat.

Eagle and Pig were unhappy
with Cat's news.

"Well," thought Eagle.

"I will not stay if I am not wantcd."

And with that, he went away
to another tree.

"I will not stay if I am not wanted,"
said Pig.

"I will find another tree."

And with that, he walked away
to find another tree.

"Now I can get some sleep," Cat said.

Cat went back up the tree
to his home.

But when night came,
he couldn't sleep.

He was so unhappy!

"What are all the night noises?
Where are my friends, Eagle and Pig?"
he thought.

Cat missed his friends.

It was no fun being in a tree
without friends!

At last the morning sun came up,
and Cat came down from the tree.

"I know what I have to do," he said.
He ran into the woods to find his friends.

"I made up the things I said about you,
Eagle," said the cat.

"And I made up the things I said
about you too, Pig."

Eagle and Pig were surprised at this.
But they still wanted to be friends with Cat.

So the eagle, the cat, and the pig
went back to the tree.

Eagle went to the top.
Cat went to his home under Eagle.
Pig went to his home under Cat.

Three in a tree!
What a good way to live!

Yoko's Turn

When Yoko's grandmother came to stay
at Yoko's house, Yoko's friends came over.

The children would sit down and have
something to eat.

Then they would take turns asking for
a story.

This day it was Yoko's turn.

" May we have a story about a—a MOUSE,
Grandmother ? " asked Yoko.

" Yes, yes, " said all the children.

" A mouse . . . , " said Yoko's grandmother.
" Let me see, a mouse. . . . "
Then she began.

Mr. and Mrs. Mouse had
a beautiful daughter.

She was so beautiful that they
named her Lovely.

Mr. and Mrs. Mouse wanted Lovely to marry
the most powerful being in the world.

So Mr. Mouse went out to find the
most powerful being in the world—the sun.

He walked and walked till he came
to where the sun lived.

" Mr. Sun, " he said.

" You are the most powerful being
in the world.

I want you to marry my daughter.

She is the most beautiful mouse
in the world. "

156

The sun laughed.

"I am not the most powerful being in the world," he said.

"Then who is?"
asked Mr. Mouse.

"Why Mr. Cloud is," said the sun.
"He can hide me."

157

Mr. Mouse went to find Mr. Cloud.

"Mr. Cloud," he said.

"You are the most powerful being
in the world.

I want you to marry my daughter.
She is the most beautiful mouse
in the world."

The cloud laughed.

"I am not the most powerful being
in the world," he said.

"Then who is?" asked Mr. Mouse.

"Why Mr. Wind is," said the cloud.

"He can blow me about as he pleases."

It was late and the wind began to blow.
Soon Mr. Wind came.

" Mr. Wind, " said the mouse.

" You are the most powerful being
in the world.

I want you to marry my daughter.

She is the most beautiful mouse
in the world. "

The wind said, " I am not the most
powerful being in the world. "

" Then who is ? " asked Mr. Mouse.

" Why the wall by your house is, "
said the wind.

" I can't blow him down. "

So Mr. Mouse went home.

He went up to the wall.

" Mr. Wall, " he said.

" You are the most powerful being
in the world.

Mr. Cloud is more powerful than Mr. Sun.

Mr. Wind is more powerful than Mr. Cloud.

And you, Mr. Wall, are more powerful than
Mr. Wind.

I want you to marry my daughter.

She is the most beautiful mouse
in the world. "

160

Mr. Wall laughed and laughed.

Then he said, "Mr. Mouse, you were looking for the most powerful being in the world.

You are it.

Yes, Mr. Mouse," he said.

"I can stand up to the wind.

The wind can blow a cloud away.

And the cloud can hide the sun.

But you can make holes.

One day you will make so many holes that I will fall down.

The mouse is the most powerful being in the world."

Mr. Mouse was surprised by what
the wall said.

He didn't know what to do.

Then he ran into the house.

He wanted Mrs. Mouse and Lovely
to know what he had learned.

His people were the most powerful beings
in the world.

162

Soon there was a big feast in the home
of Mr. and Mrs. Mouse.

Lovely married a very handsome mouse.

Every mouse was happy.

They all knew who was the most powerful
being in the world—the mouse.

Yoko's friends said, " What a good story. "

They had something more to eat
before they went home.

Whose Hat?

Who might wear this hat?

What might you know about someone who wears this hat?

What kinds of things can't you tell about someone who wears this hat?

164

Making and Choosing Words

Can you make words by putting the letters
at the left of each row in the blanks?
Write them on paper and see.

bl   __ __ack   __ __ond   __ __ast   __ __emp   __ __ame

ch   __ __air   __ __oke   __ __ ep   __ __est   __ __ill

nd   se__ __   ba__ __   le__ __   ga__ __   wi__ __

Choose two words that go together in some way.

1. mark   barn   harm   farm

2. car   harp   park   card

3. yard   start   arm   garden

4. part   bark   dark   star

Which can you do?

jump rope   hope for fun

tell a poke   jump up a pole

eat a cone   laugh at a joke

poke a hole   run home

Whirr, Rumble, and Click

Building a Road

It takes a long time to build a road.

Many workers and machines are needed.

First, people plan where the new road will go.

When the plans are finished, other people

and machines go to work.

A bulldozer is one machine that helps
to build a new road.

A bulldozer can do the work
of many, many people.

Shovels help build a road too.
They dig into the hills to get the dirt.

Big trucks carry the dirt away.
Over and over the trucks come
to carry the dirt away.

169

A machine with big round rollers works
on the new roadbed.

This machine goes over the roadbed
many times.

One machine makes little rocks
out of big ones.

Many, many rocks are needed
to build a road.

The machine with the big round rollers
goes over the rocks.

Many, many times it goes up and down
over the rocks.

Another machine puts tar on top
of the rocks.

The roller machine comes back.

'Round and 'round its rollers go
over the tar and rocks.

Now the tar and rocks will stay in place.

The last big machine puts a black top
on the new road.

The road is finished, and soon it will
take people to many places.

The Other Side of the Mountain

Jeff's Mountain

Jeff lived in a little green house
on a country road.

On the other side of the road
was a mountain.

Jeff liked to look at his side
of the mountain.

When it was fair, with the sun
on the trees,
the mountain was green.

172

At other times, when the sun went down, the mountain looked black.

Sometimes it was white with snow.

Every morning on his way to school, Jeff would look up at the mountain.

" How I wish I could go over that mountain, " he thought.

" I wish I could see what is on the other side. "

Jeff liked to guess what it was like.

But there was no road over the mountain.

There was no way for Jeff to find out.

One morning a truck stopped
at Jeff's house.

Some people got out of the truck.

A man put stakes into the road.

The woman looked at a big sheet
of paper.

For a long time the people talked and looked
at the mountain.

" That's strange, " Jeff thought.

" What are the stakes for ?

What is on that sheet of paper ?

Why are the people looking
at the mountain ? "

The woman with the sheet of paper smiled at Jeff.

" What are you doing ? " Jeff asked.

" We are going to build a road here, " said the woman.

" Will it go over the mountain ? " Jeff wanted to know.

" Yes, it will, " the woman said.

" Boy, how I wish I could go over there, " said Jeff.

" What's on the other side ? "

" You will see, " said the woman.

" It will take a long time to build the road, but one day you can ride over the mountain.

Then you will see what's on the other side. "

That day many men and machines came to work on the new road.

For a long time Jeff watched the truck and shovel and bulldozer at work.

Every day from then on, Jeff would run home from school.

He liked to watch the men building the new road.

Jeff wished the men and machines could work faster.

He couldn't wait to see what was on the other side of the mountain.

Summer came, and there was no school.

Every day Jeff watched the machines.

He liked to see the trucks come and go.

He liked the way the roller machine
rolled the rocks into place.

All the long summer days, Jeff watched
the road building.

Before long the summer was over.
Some of the trees on the mountain
were a blaze of red and yellow leaves.

Jeff watched a machine put tar
over the top of the road.

" Soon the road will be finished, " he said.

" Soon I will get my wish and see
what is on the other side of the mountain. "

One winter morning when Jeff got up,
he looked out at the mountain.
The machines were not there.
The first snow of the winter had come.
Everywhere it was white!

"Dad! Dad!" Jeff called.

"Where are the machines?

Why did the workmen stop

building the road?"

Jeff's dad looked up from his newspaper.

"Winter has come, Jeff," he said.

"The men can't work on the road now.

It says here in the paper that the men

will go back to work in the spring."

"Spring!" said Jeff.

"But spring is so far off!

When will I find out what is

on the other side of the mountain?"

Over the Mountain

The winter was long, but spring came
at last.

And with the first spring days
came the road workers.

In no time at all, the road had its
new black top.

There it was—a new road that went up and
over the mountain.

Jeff and his dad talked about the new road.

Dad said that on Saturday he would
take Jeff for a ride to see the other side
of the mountain.

Saturday came, and not too soon for Jeff !

He couldn't wait to see the other side
of the mountain !

Up, up the mountain went Dad's old car.

Jeff looked back.

How far away the little green house looked
from here !

Soon Jeff and his dad got to the top.

" Here we are, " said Dad.

" Want to get out and take a look ? "

When Jeff got out of the car, he saw a boy in a red cap watching him.

The boy waved and said, " I came up here to see what's on the other side of the mountain. "

" That's funny. So did I, " said Jeff.

Then something surprised Jeff.

The boy with the red cap was not looking the right way !

He was looking down the side of the mountain where Jeff lived.

" Look here, " said Jeff.

" We each came up to find out what was
on the other side of the mountain.

But you are not looking the right way.

I just came from that side.

I live there.

All you can find down there is a
little town. "

The boy in the red cap looked at Jeff
in great surprise.

"But you are not looking the right way.
I just came from that side of the mountain.
All that is down there is a little town."

Jeff and the boy looked at each other.

How could each side of the mountain
be like the other?

The boys smiled, and then laughed.

" Well, I got my wish, " said Jeff.

" I got my wish too, " said the boy.

" And the road did something good for us.

Now you can ride over to my side,
and I can ride over to yours.

We will be friends.

THAT'S what is on the other side
of the mountain ! "

188

The Clock

Here's what I think
about a clock:
It should be tired
ticktocking all the time—
tight-wired,
wheels whizzing,
dizzying,
hands creeping,
never sleeping.

Well, I've had it all apart
and back again,
even the main—
spring,
sort of testing
it. And now
I've fixed it somehow
so the clock is
resting.

Felice Holman

The New Machine

You go to school to learn.

There are many things in school that help you.

Books and movies help you learn.

And now there is a new machine.

This new machine is called a computer.

Before you can use the computer, someone prepares it with questions to ask you.

One way you can talk to a computer is by using a machine that may make you think of a typewriter.

It is called a teletypewriter.

The computer sends you a message through the teletypewriter.

You answer the questions using the teletypewriter.

The computer tells you if you are right or wrong.

The first thing you may do is type your name on the teletypewriter.

The computer may have the teletypewriter answer you by typing: HELLO (Your name).

Then it will ask you a question.

Or it may show you something to do.

You may type your answer.

If your answer is right, you may be asked another question.

If your answer is not right, you may be told: NO. TRY AGAIN.

Or you may be given a hint.

This is one way a computer may work.

Do you have a computer in your classroom or in your school?

If you don't, one day you may.

Then you can learn how to use it.

Clara's Barn

Clara and her mother and father lived
in the country.

They lived in a little house next
to a big barn.

Clara went to school on a bus.

The bus picked up all the children who
went to Clara's school.

All the children lived in the country too.

One day Clara's teacher showed the class pictures of barns.

They looked at the pictures and talked about how they looked.

Then the teacher asked everyone to tell about a barn they had been in.

Clara's hand went up first.

The teacher called on her.

" Our barn is a music factory, " said Clara.

" It's next to our house.

My mother and father work in it.

They make music computers in our barn. "

"Barns are for horses," said a boy in the class.

"And for hay," said a girl.

"Nobody around here makes computers," said another.

"Computers are only for reading and numbers."

"Children! Children!" said the teacher.
"One at a time, now.
Let Clara finish telling us about her barn.
Then you can ask her what you want to know.
Go on, Clara."

So Clara told the class how her mother and father made music computers.

She said that their computer was a new computer.

Clara had so much to tell and the class had so much to ask that they didn't want to stop.

" Clara, " said the teacher.

" Do you think we could see the music computer factory in your barn? "

" Oh, yes, " said Clara.

" People are always coming to see the computer.

I'll ask and find out when you can come. "

Clara's mother and father were very happy to have Clara's class come to see their factory.

They showed the class all the parts of the computer.

They showed them how they put the parts together.

Then everyone got to play the keyboard
of the music computer.

Whatever the children played, the
computer could play back in many ways.

It could play like a big band or
like a bird singing.

Whatever notes the children played
on the keyboard, the computer would show
on the TV screen.

After everyone in the class had
finished playing the computer, Clara sat
down at the keyboard.

She played the songs the children sang
in school.

Everyone sang along with the computer.
And the sound of music filled
Clara's barn.

The Steam Shovel

The steam digger
Is much bigger
   Than the biggest beast I know.
He snorts and roars
Like the dinosaurs
   That lived long years ago.

He crouches low
   On his tractor paws
And scoops the dirt up
   With his jaws;
Then swings his long
   Stiff neck around
And spits it out
   Upon the ground . . .

Oh, the steam digger
Is much bigger
   Than the biggest beast I know.
He snorts and roars
Like the dinosaurs
   That lived long years ago.

Rowena Bennett

203

What Is in the Circle?

Read the words around the circle.
Read the sentence in the circle.
Think of a word that is like the other
words and fits the sentence.

bid
bad · You sleep in one. · bud

pin
pun · Your mother cooks in one. · pen

went
bent · You camp out in one. · sent

stool
cool · A saw is one. · school

sheep
weep · You do this at night. · "cheep"

band
sand · You have a right and a left. · land

back
sack · It is a small sharp thing. · black

shop
stop · You do it on one foot. · mop

book
shook · You can hang things on it. · look

Opposites

These words are opposites.
Can you read them all?

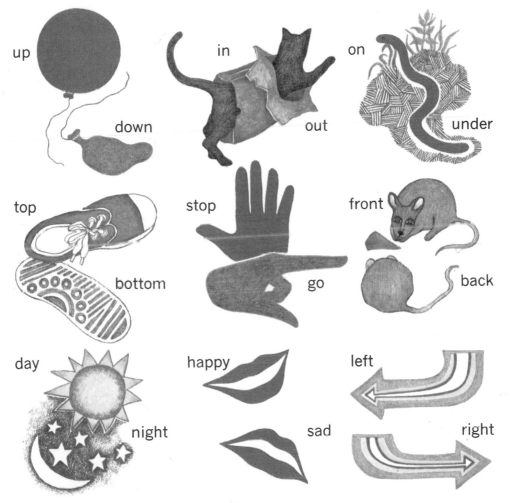

up

down

in

out

on

under

top

bottom

stop

go

front

back

day

night

happy

sad

left

right

Now draw pictures to show that these are opposites.

light	play	big	fast
dark	work	little	slow

And So It Was

The Elves and the Shoemaker

The Shoemaker

A long, long time ago, a little old man and a little old woman lived in a little old house.

In the house there was a shop where the little old man made shoes. The little old woman helped him. They were happy when they had made many shoes.

One night the little old man said to the little old woman, "We have no money. We must have money to get the leather to make the shoes. We can't make shoes without leather. What can we do?"

The little old woman didn't like
to see the little old man so unhappy.
"Don't think about it now," she said.
"We can talk about the money
for leather in the morning."

So the little old man
and the little old woman went to bed.

In the morning the shoemaker
came down into his store. There
before him were seven new pairs of shoes.
"How can this be?" the shoemaker
asked the little old woman. "Last night
I had no leather to work with.
Today I find seven new pairs of shoes!
And they are well-made shoes too.
How can this be?"

That day people came
into the shoemaker's store. They liked the
new shoes. They gave the shoemaker money.

Late that day the old man went out
to get more leather to make more shoes.
When he got back, he didn't have time
to make the shoes.

So the shoemaker went to bed.

When morning came, the shoemaker
was surprised again.

" What's this ? " he asked.

" Again I find seven new pairs
of shoes ! How did they get here ? "

Once more people came into the store
for the shoes, and once more they gave
the shoemaker money for them.

That night the old man talked
with his wife. " Tonight I won't go
to bed, " he said. " I'll stay up
and see who comes to help me
with my work. "

" I'll stay with you, " said the little
old woman. " We'll watch and see
who it is that works here for us. "

The Helpers

Soon the little old man
and the little old woman
saw something strange.

Seven little elves came into the store.
The elves jumped about and sang.
Then they began to work on the shoes.
In no time at all they had made
seven new pairs of shoes.

" Do you see what I see ? "
asked the little old man.
" The elves have no coats
and they have no shoes.
But they did all this work for us ! "

" I think we can help them, "
said the little old woman.
" I will make seven coats for them.
And you can make seven little pairs
of shoes. "

All the next day the little old man
and the little old woman worked.
They made seven little red coats
and they made seven little pairs
of red shoes.

"Let's hide and watch for the elves to come," said the shoemaker.

So that is just what they did.

When the elves came that night, they were so surprised and happy! They liked the seven little red coats. And they were happy with the shoes.

The elves put on the new things and jumped around and sang.

"Thank you, old shoemaker,"
the elves called. "Thank you too,
old woman. We helped you, for you
are good people. We will not come
again. Now you can make shoes
without us."

And no one ever saw the little elves,
not ever again.

The Gnome

I saw a Gnome
As plain as plain
Sitting on top
Of a weathervane.

He was dressed like a crow
In silky black feathers,
And there he sat watching
All kinds of weathers.

218

He talked like a crow too,
Caw caw caw,
When he told me exactly
What he saw,

Snow to the north of him
Sun to the south,
And he spoke with a beaky
Kind of a mouth.

But he wasn't a crow,
That was plain as plain
'Cause crows never sit
On a weathervane.

What I saw was simply
A usual gnome
Looking things over
On his way home.

Harry Behn

THE BOY AND THE WOLF

(An unhappy boy sits on a rock. His sheep are all around him.)

BOY: Why do I have to sit here
and watch the sheep? All day long
I just stay in this one place.
It is no fun being out here alone.

(Two men come up the hill.
The boy sees them.)

BOY: Help ! Help ! Please help me !
A wolf is going to eat my sheep !

FIRST MAN: Where ? Where is the wolf ?
Which way did he go ?

BOY: Follow me !

(The men follow the boy
to the top of the hill.)

SECOND MAN: I see many sheep, but where is
a wolf ? Which way did the wolf
go ?

BOY: There is no wolf. I played
a trick on you.

(The boy laughs.)

(The second man talks to his friend.)

SECOND MAN: This boy has tricked us.
Come, my friend. Let's get back
on our horses and ride into the city.
We have no time for this boy's tricks.

(The men ride down the hill.)

BOY: That was fun. I think I will do
it again.

(The boy runs and calls to the men.)

BOY: Help me ! Help me !
A big wolf hides here by the tree.
This is no trick. The wolf is going
to eat my sheep !

FIRST MAN: Do you want to go back ?
Maybe there is a wolf this time.

(The men ride up the hill again.)

223

SECOND MAN: There is no wolf here.

You have tricked us again.

FIRST MAN: But you will not play games

with us another time.

We are going,

and we will not come back.

(*The men ride away.*)

BOY: That was great fun.

The men thought the wolf

was going to eat my sheep !

(*The boy laughs.*)

I think I will just sit here

by the tree.

(*The boy sits under the tree.*)

224

(A wolf comes over the hill.)

WOLF: My, what beautiful white sheep
you have ! They look just right
for eating !

(The boy jumps up.)

BOY: No ! No ! You can't eat my sheep !

WOLF: There is no one here to stop me.
I can eat whatever I want. Which
one will be the first ?

(The boy runs to the top
of the hill.)

BOY: Help ! Help ! Please help me !
The wolf has come, and he is going
to eat my beautiful sheep !

FIRST MAN: Playing tricks again, is he ?
What a strange boy he is !
He can't trick us again.
We know there is no wolf.

(The men ride on.
The boy keeps calling.)

BOY: Please come ! Please ! This time
there IS a wolf !

WOLF: You see ? Now no one will help
you. That is what you get
for playing tricks !

The Mud Horses

A long time ago, the people of the Plains had no horses. Dogs were the only animals they had to help them carry things.

At that time, there lived a boy without a home. The boy would go from teepee to teepee to ask for food. Sometimes he was chased away. Sometimes he was asked in and given food.

Sometimes he would go to the place
where the chief lived.

The chief was a kind and wise man.
He would give the boy something
to wear or something else he needed.

Some of the people would try to stop
the chief from giving things to the boy.
The chief would say to them, " The boy is
one of our people. Who knows ? Someday he
may be our chief. "

But the people just laughed at that.

Now the boy without a name had wonderful dreams. One night he had a dream about horses. In his dream, two horses came down out of the sky. He knew they were for him. The horses were very close, and he could see them very well.

After he woke up, he remembered
everything about the horses. He took
some mud and began to make the horses
from his dream. He remembered the way
they looked. He remembered the shape
of their legs, the shape of their backs, and
the way their hair fell.

When he had finished the horses, he took
them down to the water and let them drink.
Then he took them to where there was good
grass and let them eat. Every day he would
take care of his mud horses, but none
of the people saw them.

One night, he had another dream.
The horses came down out of the sky again.

Then in the dream he heard someone
singing a song. He could hear the song
very well.

When he woke up, he remembered the song.
He got up and went to a high hill. There
he began to sing the song. He sang
the song from his dream.

It was a wonderful song and
all the people heard it. They heard it
and wondered who was singing it.

The boy went on singing. Then a voice
from the sky said to him, " This song is
your song. You will become a chief.
Go to the place where your mud horses are.
Go there and you will find two real horses. "

232

The boy ran and all the people followed
him. When he came to the place, he saw two
real horses. They came to him, and he took
hold of them.

The people looked at the horses
in wonder, for they were the first
they had ever seen.

Why the Sun and Moon Live in the Sky

Long ago the sun and water lived on the Earth together. They were good friends.

The sun went to visit the water many times. But the water never went to visit the sun.

" Why don't you ever come to my house to visit ? " said the sun to the water.

"Your house is too small," said the water. "If I came to visit you with all my people, we would run you out of your house. I have many, many people, and they take up a lot of room."

The sun said he would build a very big house so water and his people could come visit him.

Then he went home and told his wife, the moon. She smiled and said she would help him.

The very next day, the sun began to build a big, big house. It was soon ready.

Water and his people came to visit the sun and the moon.

When they got there, water called out
to the sun, "Is it safe to come in?"

"Yes," said the sun. "Come in, my friend."

So the water, the fish, and all
the water animals began to flow into
the sun's big house.

Soon the water was up to the window. So water asked the sun if it was still safe. The sun said yes, so more water came in.

Very soon the water was up to the top
of the door.

" Do you want more of my people
to come in ? " asked water.

".Yes, " said the sun and the moon.

So water flowed on into the house with more of his people.

Soon the sun and moon had to go up to the top of the roof.

Again water asked. Again the sun said yes.
So more and more of water's people came in.

Very soon, the water was over the top
of the roof. The sun and the moon had to go
up into the sky.

And that's where they are still.

How Do Stories Begin?

Long ago people did not understand how things came about. But they did ask questions. To answer such questions they made up their own stories. People told the stories to their children. Today we can read the stories that people made up long ago.

Indians told stories about the man in the moon. Men long ago told stories about how the sun came to be in the sky.

Can you make up a story about how something might have happened? Maybe these questions will help you.

How did the stars get up into the sky?

What makes the wind blow?

What makes day and night?

Two Make One

rail
road   railroad

black
bird   blackbird

snow
man   snowman

bed
time   bedtime

On your paper draw pictures of what the
two words make when you put them together.

wish
bone

green
house

base
ball

watch
man

Grandfather and I

Grandfather and I
are going for a walk.
It will be a slow walk
because
Grandfather and I
never hurry.
We walk along

and walk along

And stop . . .

And look . . .

just as long
as we like.

Other people we know
are always in a hurry.

Mothers hurry.

They walk in a hurry
and talk in a hurry.
And they always
want *you* to hurry.

But Grandfather and I
never hurry.
We walk along
and walk along

And stop . . .

And look . . .

just as long as we like.

Fathers hurry.
They hurry
off to work
and they hurry
home again.
They hurry
when they kiss you
and when they
take you for a ride.

But Grandfather and I
never hurry.
We walk along
and walk along

And stop . . .

And look . . .

just as long as we like.

Brothers and sisters
hurry, too.
They go so fast
they often bump into you.

And when *they* take you
for a walk
they are always
leaving you far behind.

But Grandfather and I
never hurry.
We walk along
and walk along

And stop . . .

And look . . .

just as long
as we like.

256

Things hurry . . .
Cars and buses,
trains and little boats.
They make noises
when they hurry—

They toot whistles
and blow horns.
And sometimes
scare you.

Grandfather and I never hurry.

We walk along and walk along

And stop . . .

And look . . .

just as long as we like.

260

And when Grandfather and I
get home
we sit in a chair
And rock and rock.
And sing a little . . .
And talk a little . . .
And rock and rock . . .
just as long as we like—

Until somebody
tells us to hurry.

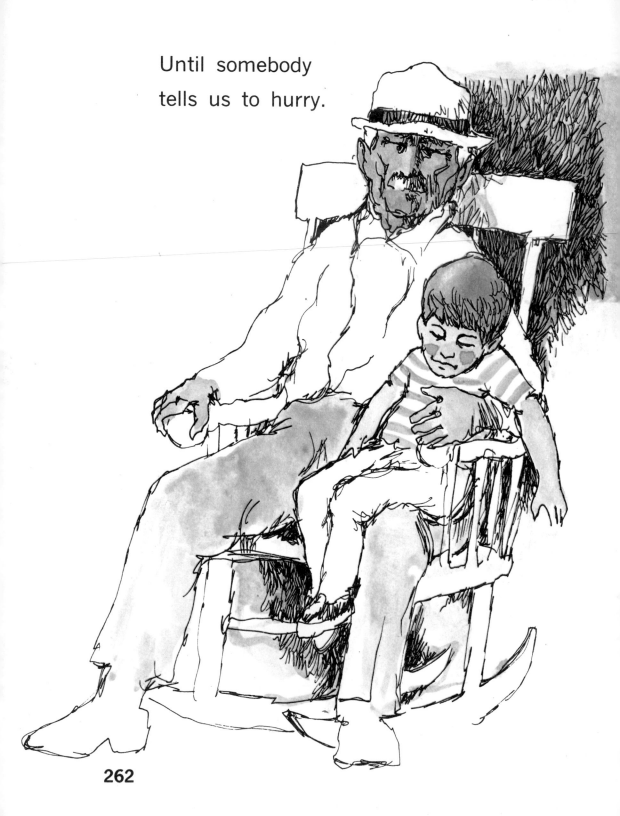

New Words in This Book

The following new words are presented in *One To Grow On,* Level Six, Reading 720. Words printed in regular type are new basic words. Those underlined are new enrichment words, and those printed in color are new words that pupils can decode independently.

UNIT 1

PAGE

8 Freckles

9 face

10 cream
   shaving

12 other
   Shorty
   sometimes

13 smile

16 about
   mine
   school
   thought
   took
   White

17 day

18 children

19 Lucy

20 Cunningham
   waved

21 Dandy
   Mrs.
   well

23 Lee

25 birthday
   magic
   seven
   today

27 apartment

28 brothers
   four
   hamster

29 night
   remember

31 May Ling
   morning
   two

32 picks
   starts
   steps

33 bookstore
   by
   father's
   or
   places
   playground
   side

34 care
   doesn't
   making
   sick

35 over

79	more		harbor		we're
	rooster	97	coming	112	Pepe
	safe	98	noise		slate
	sheep	99	someday	113	inside
80	same	100	past	114	very
	year		seen	115	place
81	began	103	flakes	116	action
	learn		soft		camera
	many		softly		closed
	women	104	daylight		ready
82	maps		pretty	117	hot
83	age		stay		Sam
	higher	105	keep		sun
	ready		policeman	118	cool
		106	snowballs	120	wash
UNIT 3		108	Juan		water
			Lola	121	or
89	sights		movie		splashed
	5th		real		wet
90	bus	109	they're		
	does	110	cable	**UNIT 4**	
91	next		poles		
92	happy		vans	128	busy
	many	111	Ana		clocks
96	boats		begin		shop

267

Illustrations and photographs were provided by the following: Franz Altschuler (208–226); Kathy Arnold (146); Philip Jon Bailey (168–171, 190–195); Tom Cooke (8–13, 16–25, 124, 125); Faith Cushing (14, 188); Masami Daijogo (80–85); Ted Rand (196–202); Lois Ehlert (48–59); Tom Garcia (128–133); Leigh Grant (155–165); Logan Holtby (134–141); John Kuzich (71–75, 77–79); Ted Lewin (108–116); David McPhail (247–262); Jane Teiko Oka (88–107, 117–123); Joan Paley (64–65, 76); Robert Quackenbush (31–43, 44, 45); Miriam Schottland (234–245); Dorothea Sierra (203–205); Donald Silverstein (147–154); Joel Snyder (172–187, 227–233); George Ulrich (66–70); Fred Witzig (142–145).

The cover and unit introduction pages were designed by Gregory Fossella Associates.

BCDEFGHIJK 79876
PRINTED IN THE UNITED STATES OF AMERICA

D